Professional ethics in accounting

Workbook

Jo Osborne
Sheriden Amos

Published by Osborne Books Limited
Unit 1B Everoak Estate
Bromyard Road, Worcester WR2 5HP
Tel 01905 748071
Email books@osbornebooks.co.uk
Website www.osbornebooks.co.uk

Design by Laura Ingham

Printed by CPI Group (UK) Limited, Croydon, CR0 4YY, on environmentally friendly, acid-free paper from managed forests.

British Library Cataloguing in Publication Data
A catalogue record for this book is available from the British Library

ISBN 978 1909173 248

Contents

Acknowledgements

The publisher wishes to thank the following for their help with the reading and production of the book: Maz Loton and Cathy Turner. Thanks are also due to Laura Ingham for her designs for this series.

The publisher is indebted to the Association of Accounting Technicians for its help and advice to our authors and editors during the preparation of this text.

Authors

Jo Osborne is a Chartered Accountant who trained with Ernst & Young in their London office. She then moved to Cable & Wireless where she spent two years in their internal audit department before moving into an investment appraisal role. Jo has taught AAT at Hillingdon College and until recently at Worcester College of Technology where she took on the role of AAT Coordinator.

Sheriden Amos is a Chartered Accountant who trained with KPMG in their Birmingham office. She then moved to KPMG Bristol, before working for five years in the finance department of Port Philip Group Ltd, part of TUI Travel PLC, ultimately becoming Finance Director. Sheriden is currently teaching on a range of professional accounting and degree courses at Worcester College of Technology.

Introduction

what this book covers

This book has been written to cover the 'Professional ethics in accounting' Unit which is mandatory for the revised (2013) AAT Level 3 Diploma in Accounting.

what this book contains

This book is set out in two sections:

- **Chapter Activities** which provide extra practice material in addition to the activities included in the Osborne Books Tutorial text. Answers to the Chapter activities are included in this book.

- **Practice Assessments** are provided to prepare the student for the Computer Based Assessments. They are based directly on the structure, style and content of the sample assessment material provided by the AAT at www.aat.org.uk. Suggested answers to the Practice Assessments are set out in this book.

further information

If you want to know more about our products and resources, please visit www.osbornebooks.co.uk for further details and access to our online shop.

Chapter activities

1 Principles of professional ethics

1.1 The document issued by the AAT providing guidance to full and student members regarding professional ethics is called which of the following?

✔

(a)	AAT Rules on Professional Ethics	
(b)	AAT Principles on Professional Ethics	
(c)	AAT Code of Professional Ethics	

1.2 Which **ONE** of the following is not an objective of the accounting profession?

✔

(a)	Mastering of particular skills and techniques acquired through learning and education and maintained through professional development	
(b)	Acknowledgement of duties to society as a whole in addition to the employer or the client	
(c)	Rendering personal services to generally accepted standards of conduct and performance	
(d)	An outlook which is essentially objective, obtained by being fair minded and free from conflicts of interest	

1.3 Which **ONE** of the following is not one of the five fundamental principles of professional ethics?

✔

(a)	Objectivity	
(b)	Confidentiality	
(c)	Professional qualification	
(d)	Integrity	

1.4   Complete the following sentence by selecting the appropriate option from the list below:

When a member is faced with a situation that he/she feels may cause a conflict of interest which could affect his/her professional judgement, he/she will have to consider the fundamental ethical principle of ....

- Integrity
- Objectivity
- Professional behaviour

1.5   Charlie works for an accounting practice. One of her clients has asked for some detailed inheritance tax advice. The firm does not have any members of staff with the necessary skills to give this advice. Which of the following fundamental principles could this most threaten?

✔

(a) Professional competence and due care	
(b) Objectivity	
(c) Professional behaviour	

1.6   A member of your accounting staff has submitted an expense claim for approval. For one client he has claimed travel expenses for a week when you are certain that he was given a lift in another member of staff's car.

(a)   Should you approve his travel expense claim? | YES/NO |

(b)   Which fundamental principle is being compromised by the member of staff in this situation?

✔

(a) Integrity	
(b) Objectivity	
(c) Professional behaviour	

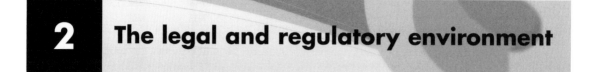

2 The legal and regulatory environment

2.1   Which branch of law does the following definition relate to?

'This results in a prosecution in court by the state of the accused for a breach of the law, such as for the crimes of theft, money laundering, terrorist financing, bribery and fraud. The consequence is punishment of the accused, if found guilty, by imprisonment or fine.'

2.2   What are the three main committees that make up the Financial Reporting Council (FRC)?

1.
2.
3.

2.3   Decide if the Code of Ethics issued by the International Ethics Standards Board for Accountants is legally enforceable.

Choose one option: | YES / NO |

2.4 State how each of the three regulated (reserved) areas in accountancy and finance detailed below are regulated.

Reserved area	Regulation
External audit	
Investment business	
Insolvency work	

2.5 Which body does the statement below describe?

'A forum in which matters affecting the accounting profession as a whole can be discussed and co-ordinated and which enables the accounting profession to speak with one voice on important matters.'

2.6 There are four accounting bodies that are sponsoring bodies of the AAT. Explain what the role of a sponsoring body involves.

2.7 The duty to comply with the five fundamental ethical principles applies to which of the following?
Choose **ONE** option.

		✔
(a)	Professional accountants in practice	
(b)	Professional accountants in business	
(c)	Professional accountants in practice and professional accountants in business	

3 **Threats and safeguards to fundamental ethical principles**

3.1 State the five types of potential threats to a professional accountant's compliance with the fundamental ethical principles and explain how they may occur.

Type of threat	How this type of threat may occur
1.	
2.	
3.	
4.	
5.	

3.2 Leandra is a professional accountant who works for a medium sized firm of accountants in Goldtown. One of her colleagues, Jacob, has recently finished a secondment to the finance department at Hastings Ltd, one of the firm's clients. During her work at Hastings Ltd she reviews the depreciation calculation prepared by Jacob and discovers a significant error in the figures.

(a) In this situation explain what two types of threat Leandra faces to her fundamental ethical principles.

1.
2.

(b) Explain which three fundamental ethical principles are most threatened by this situation.

1.
2.
3.

3.3 Eugenie has recently been appointed as the finance director of Middlematch Ltd. Prior to that she was a partner at Windsor & Clarke for fifteen years. Middlematch Ltd is a client of Windsor & Clarke and Joel Khan, a manager at Windsor & Clarke, is now about to start an assignment at Middlemarch Ltd.

Explain what type of threat this poses to Joel's fundamental ethical principles.

3.4 Esme is a professional accountant who works in practice. One of her clients, Grow-well Ltd has recently launched a new product which they claim increases the speed garden plants grow by up to 30%. The managing director of Grow-well Ltd, Jacque, has asked Esme to write a testimonial in the company's new brochure saying what an excellent product it is. He has told her that he's spoken to a friend of his who is a partner in another local accounting practice who says that were Grow-well Ltd his client he would be happy to write a testimonial for the business.

(a) Explain the three threats that Esme faces to her fundamental ethical principles.

1.
2.
3.

(b) If Esme agrees to provide Jacque with the testimonial explain which of Esme's fundamental ethical principles is most threatened by this situation.

3.5 State five safeguards that a large firm of accountants can put in place against threats to the fundamental ethical principles of its staff.

1.
2.
3.
4.
5.

3.6 Moeen is a qualified accountant who works in the finance department of Spragus Ltd. The finance director, Jonathan Rhodes, asks Moeen to come into his office. He explains that Spragus Ltd is shortly to be taken over by a large company and the deal depends on the value of the business being at least £1.5 million. As a consequence he wants Moeen to adjust the depreciation figures on some of the large machinery. He then tells Moeen that he will be part of the management team who decides on redundancies after Spragus Ltd is taken over.

(a) Explain the main threat Moeen is facing to his fundamental ethical principles.

(b) Identify **ONE** safeguard Moeen can use in this situation to reduce the threat to his fundamental ethical principles.

3.7 Pepe works for Ambrose & Harknell, a small firm of accountants. He is currently away on a residential training course for a week. A colleague has taken over his responsibilities while he is away and has found an email from a client marked urgent.

The email is as follows:

> Good morning Pepe,
>
> Please can you update me on where we are with the bank loan application you were working on for me? I hope you haven't included the fact that I have used my house as a security for the business. As we agreed I haven't mentioned any of this to Felix Ambrose and I'm sure you would prefer that I didn't. I will pay you £250 directly into your personal bank account once the loan application has been submitted.
>
> I look forward to hearing from you soon.
>
> Archie Edwards
> Managing Director
> Edwards Electricals Ltd

(a) Explain which three of Pepe's fundamental ethical principles are most threatened by the situation detailed in Archie Edwards' email.

1.
2.
3.

(b) Identify the two types of threats Pepe faces to his fundamental ethical principles?

1.
2.

4 Objectivity and the resolution of ethical conflict

4.1 *'The Code of Ethics issued by the International Ethical Standards Board for Accountants (IESBA), which is followed by all the professional accounting bodies in the UK, sets out strict rules on the value of gifts and hospitality that can be accepted.'*

Explain whether this statement is true or false.

4.2 Germaine is a professional accountant who works for Eldritch & Prior, a medium sized firm of accountants, in Woodacre. She has recently finished an assignment for one of her clients, Jessica Green, who owns an exclusive gym and sports club in Woodacre. She has received the following email from Jessica.

> Hi Germaine,
>
> Thanks very much for all your hard work on my tax return this year. I know I gave you the information very late and I was very relieved that you managed to submit the return before the deadline.
>
> I have a complimentary pass for you and your husband to use the gym and sports club for a week of your choice. As you know this is something we offer to people who are thinking of joining the club. If you did decide to join I would be happy to give you a 60% reduction in the monthly membership fees as a little thank you for all your help.
>
> I look forward to welcoming you at the club soon.
>
> Best wishes,
> Jessica

(a) Explain which of Germaine's fundamental ethical principles may be threatened by these matters.

(b) In this situation what is the best course of action for Germaine?

4.3 Andre Russell is a qualified accountant who works for Shantry Ltd. It is two weeks before the business's financial year end on 30 June. Once the rest of the staff in the accounts department have left, Andre's manager, Amy, calls him into her office and explains that there is a significant risk that no one in the business will get their year-end bonus this year. She says the reason for this is that Shantry Ltd is not going to achieve its target profit for the year. She asks Andre to include some of the sales made immediately after the year-end in the current year's sales. She says that if Andre does this she will authorise a larger bonus for him.

(a) State which three of Andre's fundamental ethical principles are threatened by this situation.

1.
2.
3.

(b) What action could Andre take in these circumstances?

(c) State under which piece of legislation Amy might be prosecuted in these circumstances.

4.4   List the four key Bribery Act 2010 penalties.

1.
2.
3.
4.

4.5   Henry works for Catray Ltd, a firm that distributes chemical fertilisers. During the year-end inventory count he identifies 20 bags of poisonous chemicals that are no longer saleable and need to be disposed of. The warehouse manager has said that he will dispose of them 'locally'. Henry is pretty sure that this means the warehouse manager is going to dump the chemicals in a local disused quarry to avoid paying the costs associated with safe disposal. When he raises this with the warehouse manager he is told that the directors of the business are aware of this and they do not have a problem with it.

(a)   Explain the conflict of loyalties that Henry faces in this situation.

(b)   What options does Henry have to deal with this conflict of loyalties?

4.6   Craig is a qualified professional accountant who works for Andrews & Roberts, a large firm of accountants in Banterbridge. The managing director of Andersen Ltd, one of Craig's clients, has recently contacted him to discuss legal action that it has brought against one of Andersen Ltd's customers, Swann & co. Craig has also received an email from the finance director of Swann & co asking for his professional advice regarding what appears to be the same legal case.

(a)   Which two of Craig's fundamental ethical principles are threatened by the fact that both Andersen Ltd and Swann & co are clients of Andrews & Roberts?

1.
2.

(b)   What process can Craig go through to resolve the ethical conflict he has in deciding how to deal with this situation?

(c)   If Craig decides to act for one of the clients explain what issues that he must consider when carrying out the assignment.

4.7   Becky is a professional accountant who works as a senior manager at Flintoff & Trott, a large accounting practice. One of the partners, Andrea Flintoff, has asked Becky to carry out some management accounting work for Pedro Smith, one of the firm's clients, who is planning to expand his business.

During the course of her work for Pedro, Becky realises that the expansion of the business relies on a large contract which he believes he is about to sign with Greengrass Ltd, another of Flintoff & Trott's clients. She also knows that Greengrass Ltd have some serious concerns over signing the contract with Pedro.

(a)   Explain which two of Becky's fundamental ethical principles are threatened by this situation?

1.
2.

(b)   What steps can Becky take to resolve the ethical conflict that she faces?

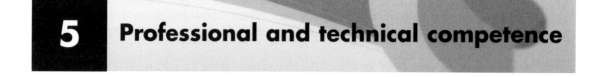

5 Professional and technical competence

5.1 **(a)** Professional accountants are expected to undertake CPD, What does the abbreviation CPD stand for?

(b) Decide which of the following statements is true.

Tick all options that apply.

		✔
(1)	It is a legal requirement for professional accountants to undertake CPD	
(2)	It is a requirement of the professional accounting bodies for accountants to undertake CPD	

5.2 State the three main ways that a professional accountant can keep up-to-date with technical changes.

1.
2.
3.

5.3 Ellery & Moss is a large firm of accountants in Temebridge. Its main business is providing taxation services to medium and large companies in and around Temebridge.

Given its client profile, state two critical areas of technical knowledge in which the staff at Ellery & Moss must keep up to date. Explain your reasons for this.

1.
2.

5.4 Milo is a professional accountant with his own small practice. He has a wide range of small clients who are mostly sole traders. For these clients he prepares sets of accounts and tax returns.

Given his client profile, explain **ONE** area of technical knowledge in which Milo must keep up to date.

5.5 Complete the following statement by inserting the correct words in the spaces.

A professional accountant who complies with the requirements to complete CPD will be helping to

protect his/her fundamental ethical principle of professional .... An

accountant who complies with the law and does not bring the accounting profession into disrepute

is complying with the fundamental ethical principle of professional ....

5.6   Eleanor is a part-qualified accountant who works for Adani Ltd. She has been working in the payroll department with Bill, a qualified accountant, who has been training her to prepare the monthly payroll. Bill has just managed to book a last minute holiday and has told Eleanor that as he is away when the payroll is due she will have to do it by herself. Eleanor does not feel confident that she can do this.

State two safeguards that Eleanor should consider to reduce the threats to her fundamental ethical principle of professional competence and due care.

1.
2.

5.7   Peter is a professional accountant in practice. His client Aaron believes that Peter has acted outside his professional competence when providing him with specific advice on accounting for imports from countries outside the European Union. As a direct result of this advice Aaron has had to pay additional import duties that he would have been able to legitimately avoid had he followed the correct procedure.

If it is proved that Peter has acted outside his professional competence, on what grounds may Aaron be able to sue Peter for this loss?

State two grounds.

1.
2.

5.8   Darius, a professional accountant in practice, has been asked by his client, Octopully Ltd, to give an opinion on their revaluation policies for the factories in Sri Lanka. Darius believes that he should visit the factories or at least contact a qualified third party in Sri Lanka for their opinion. However, Octopully Ltd are not prepared to pay the additional costs associated with a visit or a third party expert. Despite this Darius gives his opinion knowing that it is based on inadequate information.

Explain which two of Darius's fundamental ethical principles are threatened by this situation.

1.
2.

5.9   Bryony is a professional accountant in practice. Her client, Horatio, has recently completed a bank loan application. He has asked Bryony to act as a reference on the application confirming that it contains accurate information and that he will be able to make the monthly repayments on the loan.

State whether Bryony can include a disclaimer of liability with the reference that she provides.

YES / NO

5.10   Complete the following statement by inserting the correct words in the space.

Accountants should ensure that they have sufficient .... insurance to cover

against legal liability to compensate a client who has sustained a loss through a breach in the

accountant's duty of care.

6 Confidentiality and handling client money

6.1 Vernon is a professional accountant who works for Aston & Fowler, a medium sized firm of accountants. He has just accepted a job offer from Wright & Phipps, another large firm of accountants in the local area.

For each of the following situations, explain whether Vernon can disclose the information requested.

(a) Vernon's current manager at Aston & Fowler asks Vernon whether he will be paid a bigger salary at Wright & Phipps.

(b) Vernon's new manager asks him about the profitability of one of his clients at Aston & Fowler.

(c) Another member of staff at Wright & Phipps asks Vernon to explain how to complete the inheritance tax section of a client's tax return. This is a skill that Vernon learnt whist working for Aston & Fowler.

6.2   *'Professional accountants have an ethical duty to maintain confidential information about their clients however this is not a legal obligation.'*

Is this statement true or false?

TRUE / FALSE

6.3   Linus is employed by Red & Homer, a small firm of accountants. He is working on the year-end accounts for Mackenzie Ltd. During the assignment Linus learns that Mackenzie Ltd is planning a takeover of Cartwright & sons. John Mackenzie has mentioned that he has offered £400,000 for Cartwright & sons but would be willing to pay more as he knows it is worth in excess of £550,000.

Linus regularly plays golf with Allan Cartwright, who is the son of the owner of Cartwright & sons.

(a)   Should Linus tell Allan Cartwright about the information that he has gained at Mackenzie Ltd?

(b)   If Allan Cartwright asks Linus for advice about the sale to Mackenzie Ltd can Linus give him any advice?

(c)   Should Linus tell John Mackenzie about his friendship with Allan Cartwright?

6.4   Alena is an accountant in practice. She receives a telephone call from a local plumbers' merchant asking for financial information about one of her clients who has requested credit terms with them.

(a)   State whether Alena can provide the information to the plumbers' merchant.

(b)   Explain what Alena should do in these circumstances.

6.5   Yvonne Fuller is an accountant who works in practice. One of her clients, Kessler Ltd, has been in an ongoing dispute with a supplier. The supplier has now commenced legal proceedings against Kessler Ltd for non-payment for goods. Yvonne has been asked to provide copies of documents relating to this case as evidence in court and has been told that she may be required to appear in court to give evidence.

Explain whether Yvonne can provide this confidential information.

6.6   List the three circumstances in which it is acceptable for a professional accountant to disclose confidential information.

1.
2.
3.

6.7   Which legal statute (law) gives an individual the right to know what information is being held about him/her and how it is being processed?

6.8   Riley is a professional accountant who has recently set up in business as a sole practitioner. His client, Anthony, recently received a tax refund from HMRC which has been paid to Riley. Anthony is currently on holiday for two months and has not yet paid Riley's fees.

(a)   In what legal capacity is Riley holding this money for Anthony?

(b)   Explain whether Riley can use the money that he is holding for Anthony to pay his fees.

6.9 Frankie is a professional accountant in practice. He has been asked by a new client, Quentin, to hold £17,000 for him to pay his tax bill to HM Revenue & Customs which will be due in three months. Quentin hands the £17,000 to Frankie in cash. When Frankie asks where the money has come from Quentin says that he would prefer not to say. Frankie carried out all the necessary customer due diligence before taking on Quentin as a client.

(a) Explain whether Frankie can hold this money for Quentin.

(b) State what crime Frankie could be charged with if he decides to hold the money for Quentin and pay his tax bill when it falls due?

7 Codes of conduct and organisational values

7.1 State the four types of event risk that can arise from the way in which a business operates and give an example of each.

Risk	Example
1.	
2.	
3.	
4.	

7.2 Ryan is a qualified accountant working as a manager in the credit control department of Fischer Ltd. He has just been asked by the finance director to issue a large credit note to one of their customers, Stan Smith. The finance director has not provided Ryan with any supporting documentation for this credit note and there is nothing that Ryan is aware of on Stan Smith's account that would require a credit note. Ryan is aware that Stan Smith is a close friend of the finance director and they regularly play tennis together.

Explain the ethical issues that Ryan faces in this situation and what he should do to address these.

7.3 Martha Wren is the managing director of Wren Plaster Mouldings Ltd which has recently joined the Plaster Mouldings Trade Association. As part of its membership Martha has received a detailed set of best practice guidelines, which mostly relate to the accounting and payroll functions of the business. She has approached her accountants Butcher & Evans for advice on how to implement these guidelines in a code of practice for the company.

(a) List the five key organisational ethical values that Wren Plaster Mouldings Ltd should include in its code of practice.

Organisational ethical value	Point(s) where covered*
1.	
2.	
3.	
4.	
5.	

* This column is for your answers to part (b) on the next page.

(b) Butcher & Evans have produced the following draft code for Wren Plaster Mouldings Ltd. Identify which point or points in the draft code of practice below covers each of the five key organisational ethical values you have identified in part (a) above. You should write the point number or numbers in the column headed 'Point(s) where covered' on the opposite page.

Extract from draft Code of Practice for the accounting function of Wren Plaster Mouldings Ltd

Produced by: Edmund Whiteside, Senior Accountant, Butcher and Evans

All members of staff in the accounting and payroll functions will ensure that:

1. Personal information held in the accounting function will only be used for the purpose for which it was obtained and will be treated with respect and in line with relevant statutory requirements.

2. Any request for information from, staff, customers, suppliers or regulators will be treated in a timely manner and with openness, honesty, accuracy and respect.

3. Any complaint from Wren Plaster Mouldings Ltd employees about the amount or timing of a salary payment will be reviewed and responded to within 2 working days of its receipt in the payroll function.

4. Payments made to all suppliers regardless of their size or influence with the business will be made no later than 30 days after the relevant invoice has been received or in line with the supplier's credit terms if they differ from this.

5. Suppliers will be paid a fair purchase price for all goods and services.

6. Gifts or hospitality will not be accepted by any member of staff from a supplier or customer or any individual associated with Wren Plaster Mouldings Ltd unless it can be demonstrated that the same offer is made to all or substantially all of the individual's business associates. Any gift or hospitality valued at more than £50 cannot be accepted under any circumstances.

7.4 Explain whether when a business decides to implement a code of conduct it will be legally enforceable.

```


```

7.5 *'The ethical atmosphere created in the workplace by the organisation's leadership.'*

What does the statement above describe?

```


```

7.6 **(a)** Failure by a professional accountant to comply with applicable regulations and codes of practice may result in disciplinary action by which two bodies?

1.

2.

(b) State the two main categories of misconduct for which a professional accountant may be disciplined.

1.

2.

7.7   Maurice is a qualified accountant who works as a sole practitioner. He has recently started work on the year-end accounts for his client Richland Trading Ltd. During his work he discovers a number of payments that have been made to an overseas company that he does not recognise. There is no detailed supporting documentation for these payments. Maurice searches for the company on the internet but only finds a PO Box number for mail deliveries.

Maurice is beginning to suspect that these payments may relate to terrorist activities.

(a)   What should Maurice do in these circumstances?

(b)   What are the consequences for Maurice of failing to act correctly in this situation?

7.8 **(a)** State the three key pieces of legislation/regulations that relate to money laundering.

1.
2.
3.

(b) State the maximum penalties that an individual could face if found guilty of 'failure to report' money laundering or terrorist financing.

(c) State the name of the document that a sole practitioner should use to report money laundering to the Serious Organised Crime Agency (SOCA).

(d) State three things that must be included in the report identified in (c).

1.
2.
3.

7.9 Niamh is a qualified accountant who works for Harding & Hadley, an accounting practice in Dealborough. She has just agreed, in principle, to take on a new client, Lucinda Smyth, who runs a successful catering business in Dealborough. Lucinda's husband Monty is also a partner in the business although he does not take an active part in running it. Although Niamh has met Lucinda socially she has never dealt with her husband.

State the customer due diligence (CDD) procedures that Niamh should carry out before she can take Lucinda on as a client.

7.10 Noah is an accountant who works for a medium sized firm of accountants. He is currently completing some tax work for his client Maya. He has just realised that Maya owes HMRC a substantial sum of money for income tax on share dividends that she did not declare on her previous year's tax return.

When Noah raises this with Maya she refuses to declare the income saying that she has recently received a letter from HMRC confirming that they have agreed her previous year's return so she does not see why she should have to pay them the tax Noah says she owes.

(a) Explain what Noah must do in this situation.

(b) What are the consequences for Noah if he does not take any action in this situation?

8 Sustainability

8.1 **(a)** State the name of the report that identifies the three key objectives of sustainable development.

(b) What are the three key objectives of sustainability and sustainable development that are set out in this report?

1.
2.
3.

(c) According to this report what is the definition of sustainable development?

8.2 An increasing number of organisations in the UK are deciding to publish a CSR report.

(a) What does the abbreviation CSR stand for?

(b) What information is normally included in a CSR report?

(c) Give **ONE** reason why a business might decide to publish a CSR report.

8.3 Byron is a professional accountant who works for Tennyson & Owen, a medium sized practice, in Teetertown. His manager, Oswald, has recently returned from an ethics update course run by his professional accounting body. He tells Byron that he must promote an ethics-based culture within Tennyson & Owen and champion sustainability. Byron is not at all sure what Oswald is talking about.

(a) Explain what Oswald means by 'promoting an ethics-based culture' and 'championing sustainability'.

Oswald then goes on to mention the 'triple bottom line', and how important this is to Tennyson & Owen's clients. Byron has no idea what Oswald means but does not want to ask for fear of looking ill-informed.

(b) Explain what Oswald means by the 'triple bottom line' for Tennyson & Owen's clients.

8.4   Simon, the managing director of Gleeson Ltd, has been discussing the performance of the business with his accountant, Ralph. He is very concerned about the possibility that a negative news report is likely to break about Gleeson Ltd's use of child workers in one of its overseas factories. This is likely to adversely affect Gleeson Ltd's reputation.

(a)   State which of the three objectives of sustainability and sustainable development is compromised by the situation that Gleeson Ltd finds itself in.

(b)   Explain what is meant by the term 'reputational risk' and how this is potentially affected by an organisation's attitude to Corporate Social Responsibility.

8.5 Paula is a professional accountant who works in the accounts department of Saunders Supplies Ltd, a business that imports coffee beans and cocoa beans. A number of customers of the business have been asking about the business's 'green policies'. This has prompted the managing director, Ralph, to ask Paula to explain how he might encourage sustainability and sustainable development in the business.

Explain four of the six key areas where Saunders Supplies Ltd should encourage sustainability and sustainable development, and give an example of action that the business can take to support each one.

1.

2.

3.

4.

Chapter activities answers

1 Principles of professional ethics

1.1 (c) AAT Code of Professional Ethics

1.2 (c) Rendering personal services to generally accepted standards of conduct and performance

1.3 (c) Professional qualification

1.4 When a member is faced with a situation that he/she feels may cause a conflict of interest which could affect his/her professional judgement he/she will have to consider the fundamental ethical principle of **objectivity**.

1.5 (a) Professional competence and due care

1.6 **(a)** No

    (b) (a) Integrity

2 The legal and regulatory environment

2.1   Criminal law

2.2   1.   Codes and Standards Committee

2.   Conduct Committee

3.   Executive Committee

2.3   No

2.4

Reserved area	Regulation
External audit	Audit Regulations and Guidance Companies Act
Investment business	Financial Conduct Authority
Insolvency work	Insolvency Act 1986

2.5   Consultative Committee of Accountancy Bodies (CCAB)

2.6   AAT sponsoring bodies work closely with the AAT to ensure a consistent approach to accounting work and also to facilitate AAT members' progression to qualification with one of the sponsoring bodies.

2.7   (c)   Professional accountants in practice and in business

3 Threats and safeguards to fundamental ethical principles

3.1

Type of threat	How this type of threat may occur
1. Self-interest threats	These may occur where a financial or other interest will inappropriately influence the member's judgment or behaviour
2. Self-review threats	These may occur when a previous judgement needs to be re-evaluated by the member responsible for that judgement
3. Advocacy threats	These may occur when a member promotes a position or opinion to the point that subsequent objectivity may be compromised in the future
4. Familiarity threats	These may occur when, because of a close or personal relationship, a member becomes too sympathetic to the interests of others
5 Intimidation threats	These may occur when a member may be deterred from acting objectively by threats; whether actual or perceived

3.2　(a)　1.　Self-review threat – Leandra is reviewing work that has been produced by Jacob who works for the same firm as she does.

　　　　　2.　Self-interest threat – as Leandra is reviewing work that has been produced by another member of staff at the firm she works for, she is facing a self-interest threat. Highlighting Jacob's error could make her firm's staff look incompetent and jeopardise the future relationship with Hastings Ltd. This also represents a self-interest threat as the loss of the client would have a direct impact on the firm's fee income.

　　　(b)　1.　Objectivity – the self-interest threat will affect Leandra's objectivity.

　　　　　2.　Professional competence and due care – if Leandra does not report Jacob's error this would be considered a lack of professional competence and due care on the part of her firm.

　　　　　3.　Professional behaviour – if Leandra is aware of the error that Jacob has made the failure to report the error would be considered unprofessional behaviour.

3.3　This is a familiarity threat to Joel's fundamental principles due to the close relationship that Eugenie previously had with the staff at Windsor & Clarke and the fact that she is now in a position of significant influence at Middlemarch Ltd.

3.4 **(a)** 1. Advocacy threat – if Esme agrees to provide the testimonial for Grow-well Ltd she would be supporting the client and so would be facing an advocacy threat to her fundamental ethical principles.

2. Intimidation threat – the managing director is putting pressure on Esme to provide his business with the testimonial.

3. Self-interest threat – the managing director is giving a strong indication that if Esme does not give Grow-well Ltd the testimonial he may dismiss her as its accountant and employ his friend's firm.

(b) If Esme agrees to provide Jacque with the testimonial her independence and hence objectivity will be most threatened.

3.5 The following is a detailed list of the safeguards a firm could put in place. Any five from this list would be an acceptable answer to this question.

- a leadership culture in the accounting practice that stresses how important it is for staff to comply with the fundamental ethical principles

- a leadership culture in the practice that expects all members of staff working on assurance assignments to act in the public interest

- strong quality control procedures which are monitored for all engagements together with a member of senior management being given responsibility for overseeing the adequate functioning of this quality control system

- documented internal policies and procedures requiring compliance with the fundamental ethical principles and a disciplinary mechanism to promote this compliance

- specific, documented policies for identifying threats to compliance with fundamental principles including evaluating the significance of these threats, and devising safeguards to eliminate these threats or reduce them to an acceptable level

- timely communication of a firm's policies and procedures, including any changes to them, to all partner and professional staff, and appropriate training and education on such policies and procedures

- documented independence policies for assurance engagements to ensure that the independence of members of staff is not threatened at any stage

- policies and procedures that will enable the identification of interests or relationships between members of staff and clients

- policies and procedures to monitor and, if necessary, manage the reliance on fees received from a single client

- using different partners on engagement teams with separate reporting lines to provide non-assurance services to an assurance client

- policies and procedures that prohibit individuals who are not members of an engagement team from inappropriately influencing the outcome of an engagement

- advising partners and professional staff of assurance clients that the practice and its members of staff must be independent from the client

- published policies and procedures to encourage and empower staff to communicate to senior levels within the firm any issue relating to compliance with fundamental ethical principles that concern them

3.6   **(a)**   Intimidation threat – the finance director is attempting to influence Moeen's behaviour and also is suggesting that he may be made redundant if he does not comply with his wishes.

   (b)   If it is possible Moeen should use the firm's internal reporting procedures to raise this issue with another director of Spragus Ltd. If this is not possible because the other directors are also keen to improve the value of the business then Moeen should take advice from his professional accounting body's advice line.

3.7   **(a)**   1.   Integrity – omitting the fact that Archie has used his house as security for the business means that Pepe is involved with providing misleading information, which is dishonest.

      2.   Objectivity – the offer of payment from Archie represents undue pressure, which may affect Pepe's professional judgement.

      3.   Professional behaviour – submitting misleading information to the bank is dishonest and therefore brings the accounting profession into disrepute.

   (b)   1.   Intimidation threat – Pepe faces an intimidation threat from Archie as he is suggesting he may tell his employers if he does not do as he asks.

      2.   Self-interest threat – Pepe faces a self-interest threat from the offer of £250 for completing the loan application.

4 Objectivity and the resolution of ethical conflict

4.1   False.

The Code of Ethics issued by IESBA gives guidance to professional accountants about using their professional judgement to decide whether they can accept gifts and hospitality. It does not set out strict values above which they cannot be accepted.

4.2   **(a)**   Jessica is offering Germaine two gifts. In this situation Germaine's objectivity may be threatened which could influence any future decisions that she makes in relation to her client, Jessica, and affect her independence.

(b)   Germaine must use her professional judgement to decide whether she can accept either of these gifts from her client, Jessica.

- The free weekly pass is something that Jessica's gym offers to anyone who is interested in joining the gym. If she wants to use the gym facilities she can therefore accept this gift without compromising her objectivity.

- The offer of a 60% discount on her gym membership is very generous and in her experience of working with Jessica is not something that is normally offered to customers. Germaine should decide that she cannot accept this gift and therefore thank Jessica for her kind offer but politely decline.

4.3   **(a)**   1.   Objectivity

2.   Integrity

3.   Professional behaviour

(b)   The offer that Amy has made constitutes an inducement, which she is offering in an attempt to influence Andre's behaviour. In the first instance Andre should tell Amy that he is not prepared to do as she asks. Depending on the amount of pressure that Amy continues to put on him Andre could:

- raise the matter with another director in the business

- inform a third party such as Andre's professional accounting body

- take legal advice

(c)   Amy could be prosecuted under the bribery act if it can be proved that she was offering Andre an enhanced bonus to influence him to do something beneficial to her.

4.4   1.   Bribing another

2.   Receiving a bribe

3.   Bribing a foreign official

4.   Failure to prevent bribery

4.5   **(a)**   Henry is employed by Catray Ltd and therefore is expected to be loyal to his employer; however he also has a duty of loyalty to his profession. The business is acting illegally by dumping the chemicals and not disposing of them safely. This is contrary to Henry's fundamental ethical principles of integrity and professional behaviour.

(b)   He should try to resolve the difference of opinion with the warehouse manager.

Despite what the warehouse manager says about the directors being happy with this behaviour Henry should raise this issue with a more senior member of staff at Catray Ltd and try to persuade them not to act illegally.

If Catray Ltd has a formal dispute resolution process Henry should consider using this to escalate the issue.

Henry can also consult with his professional accounting body and take legal advice.

Ultimately if there are no other options open to Henry he may have to offer to resign from Catray Ltd.

4.6   **(a)**   1.   Objectivity – giving advice to both clients when they are in a legal dispute would be very difficult for Craig. Even if he manages to remain independent it could appear to each of the two clients that he is favouring the other.

2.   Confidentiality – it will be difficult for Craig to keep information about each client confidential. Again, each client may perceive that he will use confidential information about it to benefit the other.

(b)   The process Craig should go through is:

•   consider the relevant facts and ethical issues that this situation raises

•   establish whether Andrews & Roberts has a set procedure for dealing with conflicts of interest between clients

•   decide what alternative courses of action are available to him

•   select the course of action that is most consistent with his fundamental principles

•   discuss the issue with senior management at Andrews & Roberts and document the issue and the discussion

(c)   It is very unlikely that the threats to Craig's fundamental ethical principles can be eliminated or reduced to an acceptable level so that he can act for one of these clients. However, if he decides that he can act for one of the two clients he must consider what safeguards he can put in place so that his relationship with the other client does not affect his professional judgement and his objectivity. These safeguards must also ensure that he does not breach the other client's confidentiality.

4.7 **(a)** 1. Confidentiality – Becky must be careful not to use confidential information gained from her work with Greengrass Ltd to advise Pedro.

2. Professional competence and due care – due care is the key issue in this situation; Becky does not want to compromise her professional competence and due care by failing to advise Pedro of the risks of relying on the contract with Greengrass Ltd.

(b) • gather all the relevant facts

• assess the ethical issues that this situation raises

• consider whether Flintoff & Trott has an established procedure (formal or informal) for the resolution of ethical conflicts, this may include reporting the issue to a more senior member of staff, probably Andrea Flintoff

• decide what alternative courses of action are available to her. This could involve explaining to Pedro that Flintoff & Trott already act for Greengrass Ltd and that their professional competence and confidentiality could be compromised if they continue to act for him

• formally discuss the issue with senior management at Flintoff & Trott and document the issue and the discussion

5   Professional and technical competence

5.1   **(a)**   Continuing Professional Development

(b)   (2)   It is a requirement of the professional accounting bodies for accountants to undertake CPD

5.2   1.   Reading professional journals

2.   Enrolling on updating courses

3.   Complying with continuing professional development requirements (CPD) for professional accountants

5.3   Any two of the following:

- changes in taxation legislation
- changes in relevant criminal law including bribery, fraud and money laundering regulations
- changes in ethical codes

Ellery & Moss primarily provides taxation services to its clients; therefore staff must be kept up-to-date on this critical area. Given the complex nature of taxation services they must also be up-to-date with changes to criminal law including bribery, fraud, and most importantly, money laundering regulations. As its clients may wish to minimise the tax they pay, the staff must also have a clear understanding of what is acceptable ethical behaviour and what is not.

As Ellery & Moss do not provide accounting services this is not critical.

5.4   Milo should keep up to date with the following (one answer):

- regulation of accounting
- tax legislation
- money laundering regulations
- financial reporting standards

Milo primarily provides services to sole traders; these businesses must comply with requirements for accurate accounts preparation and tax returns. Milo must also protect himself against the risk of money laundering.

Other areas such as auditing, company legislation, changes in ethical codes and changes in other areas of criminal law such as bribery and fraud are not critical areas for Milo's business.

5.5   A professional accountant who complies with the requirements to complete CPD will be helping to protect his/her fundamental ethical principle of professional **competence and due care.** An accountant who complies with the law and does not bring the accounting profession into disrepute is complying with the fundamental ethical principle of professional **behaviour.**

5.6   Two safeguards from the following:

- obtain additional advice or training from another member of staff in the payroll department

- ensure that she has additional time to complete the work (if this will help)

- obtain assistance from someone with the necessary expertise

- consult with a more senior member of staff at Adani Ltd, an independent expert or her accounting body

5.7   1.   Breach of contract

2.   Professional negligence

5.8   1.   Integrity – Darius is not acting honestly if he knows that he has inadequate information but stills give an opinion.

2.   Professional competence and due care – by giving an opinion without having access to adequate information Darius is not acting diligently or in accordance with applicable professional standards.

5.9   Yes, Bryony can include a disclaimer.

5.10 Accountants should ensure that they have sufficient **professional indemnity** insurance to cover against legal liability to compensate a client who has sustained a loss through a breach in the accountant's duty of care.

6 Confidentiality and handling client money

6.1 **(a)** This information is personal to Vernon so unless he has been specifically asked by the management of Wright & Phipps not to disclose it Vernon can choose whether he tells his current manager about the salary he will be paid by Wright & Phipps.

(b) Vernon has a duty of confidentiality to his clients that extends to the period after the relationship has ended so he cannot disclose this information to his new manager.

(c) Vernon is allowed to use general knowledge and experience gained from previous employment but not specific information that is covered by his duty of confidentiality to the employer or clients. Therefore he can explain how to complete the inheritance tax section of a client's tax return to his new colleague.

6.2 False. Accountants have an ethical duty and a legal obligation to maintain confidential information.

6.3 **(a)** Linus has a duty of confidentiality to his client, Mackenzie Ltd, and so should not disclose any information he has gained about his client unless he has been given specific authority to do so.

(b) Linus should explain to Allan that Mackenzie is a client of Red & Homer and in order to maintain his independence Linus suggests that Allan obtains independent advice.

(c) As soon as Linus becomes aware that John Mackenzie is planning to buy Cartwright & sons he should inform John Mackenzie of his friendship with Allan Cartwright. He should explain that he is fully aware of his duty of confidentiality regarding information he has obtained about Mackenzie Ltd. This will protect Linus from the possibility of being accused of using confidential information to advise Allan Cartwright on the sale.

6.4 **(a)** No Alena should not provide the information to the plumbers' merchant without specific authority from her client.

(b) Alena should request authority from her client to disclose the information. Verbal authority is acceptable, but it would be better if this authority were given in writing. If she obtains this authority she can then give the confidential information to the plumbers' merchant. She should include a disclaimer making it clear that this is for the use of the plumbers' merchant only and is given purely to help them to make a decision about whether or not to supply goods on credit to the client. She should also explain that the information is given without any financial responsibility on the part of her firm of accountants.

6.5 The information that Yvonne has been asked to provide is confidential. She should first ask for permission from Kessler Ltd to provide the information in court. However, if Kessler Ltd refuses she has a legal obligation to comply with the court's request so she must breach her duty of confidentiality to her client.

6.6 1. When authorised by a client or employer

2. When disclosure is required by law

3. Where there is a professional duty to disclose

6.7 The Data Protection Act 1998

6.8 **(a)** As a trustee (ie in trust for the client).

(b) No. Riley cannot use the money he is holding in trust on behalf of a client, Anthony, to pay his fees unless it has been specifically arranged with the client.

6.9 **(a)** No, Frankie cannot hold the money for Quentin unless he is satisfied that it has been obtained from a legitimate source.

(b) Money laundering.

7 Codes of conduct and organisational values

7.1

Risk	Example
Physical event risk	The risk of fire or flood which could damage documents or assets or interrupt business.
Social event risk	The risk of a business using inexpensive labour in overseas factories where employees do not have decent working conditions and could be reported negatively.
Political event risk	The risk of governments making political decisions such as increasing rates of taxation.
Economic event risk	The risk of the Bank of England increasing interest rates which would then impact on the rate of interest charged by lenders.

The examples given above are suggestions; any sensible example of each type of risk would be acceptable.

7.2   Ryan appears to have identified possible unethical behaviour on the part of the finance director as there seems to be no valid reason for issuing Stan Smith with a credit note. This puts Ryan in a difficult position due to the senior position that the finance director holds at Fischer Ltd. Ryan should gather together all the information relating to the credit note and present it to another director of the business explaining his concerns regarding the situation. If the other director does not deal with the situation then Ryan should consider taking advice from his professional accounting body as to what further action he should take.

In this situation Ryan should not simply process the credit note as this would be contrary to his fundamental ethical principles.

7.3   **(a)**   1.   Being transparent with colleagues, customers and suppliers

2.   Reporting financial and regulatory information clearly and on time

3.   Being open and honest by identifying when it is appropriate to accept and give gifts and hospitality

4.   Paying suppliers a fair price and on time

5.   Providing fair treatment, decent wages and good working conditions

(b) 1. Being transparent with colleagues, customers and suppliers – point 2

2. Reporting financial and regulatory information clearly and on time – point 2

3. Being open and honest by identifying when it is appropriate to accept and give gifts and hospitality – point 6

4. Paying suppliers a fair price and on time – points 4 and 5

5. Providing fair treatment, decent wages and good working conditions points – 1 and 3

7.4 In order for a code of conduct to be legally enforceable it must be created by legislation or regulation and will apply to a wide number of organisations. There may be elements within the code that are based on law and which could result in criminal prosecution for example requirements under health and safety regulation or relating to the Equality Act 2010 which protects against discrimination.

7.5 'Tone at the top.'

7.6 **(a)** 1. The individual accountant's professional accounting body

2. The Financial Reporting Council (FRC)

(b) 1. Bringing the accounting profession into disrepute

2. Acting in breach of the rules and regulations of the accountant's professional body

7.7 **(a)** As Maurice is a sole practitioner he will not have a Money Laundering Reporting Officer (MLRO) to whom he can report his concerns. He should, therefore, report his concerns to the Serious Organised Crime Agency (SOCA) using a Suspicious Activity Report (SAR).

(b) Failure to do this could result in Maurice himself being charged with terrorist financing offences. He should not inform anyone at Richland Trading Ltd of his suspicions.

7.8 **(a)** 1. The Proceeds of Crime Act (POCA)

2. The Terrorism Act 2000

3. The Money Laundering Regulations 2007

(b) Up to five years imprisonment and/or a fine.

(c) Suspicious Activity Report (SAR).

(d) Three of the following:

- the identity of the suspected person (if known) including full name, address, telephone numbers, passport details, date of birth, account details

- information on which the suspicion of money laundering is based

- the whereabouts of the laundered property if it is known

- details of the person making the SAR; this will normally be the Money Laundering Reporting Officer (MLRO) or sole practitioner

7.9   Niamh should verify Lucinda's identity by looking at documents, data or other information obtained from a reliable source eg her passport.

Niamh should ensure that she fully understands who the beneficial owners of the business are; in this case Lucinda's husband Monty. She should also verify Monty's identity.

Niamh should find out what Lucinda wants from the professional relationship with her (in practice this will have been discussed prior to Niamh agreeing to take Lucinda on as a client).

Niamh must ensure that she keeps written documentation of the CDD that she carries out for Lucinda and Monty.

7.10   (a)   Noah must tell Maya that he can no longer act for her. This is because the money that she has not paid to HMRC constitutes criminal property and by retaining it Maya could be charged with money laundering. Noah must not tell Maya why he can no longer act for her as this could constitute 'tipping off' which may prejudice a money laundering investigation. As Noah works for a medium sized firm of accountants he must make an internal report to the Money Laundering Reporting Officer (MLRO) who will then submit a Suspicious Activity Report (SAR) to the Serious Organised Crime Agency (SOCA).

(b)   If Noah continues to act for Maya then he is facilitating her retention of the money she should have paid to HMRC. In this situation Noah could also be accused of money laundering. He may also be guilty of the crime of failure to disclose.

8 Sustainability

8.1 **(a)** The Brundtland Report.

(the answer 'Our Common Future' would also be accepted)

(b) 1. Economic growth

2. Environmental protection

3. Social equality

(c) 'Development that meets the needs of the present without compromising the ability of future generations to meet their own needs.'

8.2 **(a)** Corporate Social Responsibility.

(b) A CSR report details how the organisation takes responsibility for supporting sustainable development through the way in which it operates and its policies and procedures. It also measures to what extent it has achieved its CSR objectives.

(c) The public and investors are keen to see a business's attitude to sustainability and will look more favourably on organisations which have made progress towards achieving their CSR goals.

8.3 **(a)** Sustainability inherently relies on management of an organisation acting in an ethical manner. It focuses on achieving the business's current aims without jeopardising its long-term needs. Professional accountants must act ethically in all aspects of their working life and in addition to this, should actively encourage and promote an ethics-based culture that discourages unethical or illegal practices. However, accountants must also remain objective and give equal consideration to all relevant issues before making an ethical decision.

(b) The 'triple bottom line' refers to the three objectives of the Brundtland report. Oswald means that Tennyson & Owen and its staff should take social, environmental and financial factors into account when measuring the position and performance of its clients and when assisting with their decision-making.

8.4 **(a)** Social equality.

(b) Reputational risk is the risk of loss resulting from damage to an organisation's reputation.

An organisation will include its sustainability targets in its Corporate Social Responsibility (CSR). When it produces a CSR report this will show its progress towards these targets. There is a risk to an organisation's reputation if it reports negative results. However the fact that a business is prepared to report its progress towards its sustainability targets and CSR will have a positive effect on its reputation.

8.5 The answer should detail four of the six points below with a sensible example of each.

Products and services – Saunders Supplies Ltd should ensure that their products or services are produced from sustainably resourced materials.

> *example* – Saunders Supplies Ltd imports coffee beans and cocoa beans, they should investigate where these products are grown to ensure that the farming methods do not damage the environment, for example by deforestation.

Customers – Saunders Supplies Ltd should ensure that they supply to their customers in a sustainable manner.

> *example* – this could be by using recycled packaging material or through environmentally friendly delivery methods such as lower carbon emission vehicles.

Employees – Saunders Supplies Ltd should encourage good working conditions for their staff and encourage their staff to take appropriate qualifications if they wish.

> *example* – all members of the accounts department should be offered the opportunity to enrol on accounting courses which should be part or fully funded by the business.

The workplace – Saunders Supplies Ltd should introduce environmentally friendly initiatives in the workplace.

> *example* – introduce recycling policies in the offices, encourage conservation of energy and then monitor the participation of staff in the schemes to measure their success.

The supply chain – Saunders Supplies Ltd should source their coffee and cocoa beans from ethically responsible suppliers.

> *example* – Saunders Supplies Ltd should buy coffee and cocoa beans that have the Fairtrade certification. This demonstrates that farmers producing the coffee and cocoa have been paid a reasonable price for their products.

Business functions and processes – Saunders Supplies Ltd must regularly review the way in which it operates to ensure it continues to support and encourage sustainability and sustainable development.

> *example* – for each of the points 1-5 above Saunders Supplies Ltd should carry out regular reviews and measure the extent to which the business is achieving its sustainability targets.

Practice assessment 1

Instructions to candidates

To 'state' something, you need to answer with a fact. If you are asked to 'explain' something you need to state the relevant fact and then give brief reason(s) for why that fact is the right answer. If you are asked to 'describe' you should set out what is involved without further explanation.

Task 1

(a) Which global body issues guidance to support accountants and professional accounting bodies all over the world?

(b) Which government agency will ultimately be informed in a situation where money laundering is suspected?

(c) State two of the three committees that make up the Financial Reporting Council (FRC) Board, the UK's independent regulator of the accounting profession.

(1)
(2)

(d) The Consultative Committee of Accounting Bodies (CCAB) provides a forum in which matters affecting the accounting profession as a whole can be discussed and co-ordinated and enables the profession to speak with one voice on important matters. State two bodies that are members of the CCAB.

(1)
(2)

(e) Professional Accountants must comply with the code of ethics, as well as with both civil and criminal law. Explain the difference between civil and criminal law.

Task 2

(a) Professional accountants are required to undertake continuing professional development (CPD). Under AAT regulations how often must a member carry out the AAT CPD cycle?

___

(b) Accountants should be honest and straightforward when dealing with other parties, such as clients, suppliers and customers. By doing this which fundamental ethical principle are they complying with?

___

(c) Charlie is a professional accountant in practice. For several years he has provided accounting services to Finleys Ltd, a family firm that makes kitchen equipment. Finleys Ltd have recently secured several large orders from two national retail chains and are looking for someone to invest extra capital in the business. Charlie's wife, Susanne, has recently inherited some money and wants to invest it in a suitable business.

(1) State whether it is acceptable for Susanne to invest in Finleys Ltd.

___

(2) If Susanne does invest and Charlie continues to work for Finleys Ltd, which of his fundamental ethical principles may be threatened? Explain the type of threat that he faces.

___

(3) Explain **ONE** possible safeguard that Charlie could use to deal with this threat.

___

(d) Nikki, a newly qualified accountant works for a small practice. She has been asked to complete a client's personal tax return by her manager who is very busy with other clients. Nikki has previously only ever completed personal tax returns as part of her accounting studies.

(1) State which of Nikki's fundamental ethical principles is most threatened in this situation.

(2) Explain what action Nikki could take to enable her to complete the return.

Task 3

Bradley is a professional accountant who has recently set up as a sole practitioner. His first client, Anya, has given him £3,000 to hold for her until she needs to pay HM Revenue & Customs (HMRC).

(a) Prior to accepting Anya as a client and holding any money for her, what process should Bradley undertake?

(b) Currently Bradley only has one business account set up at the bank. He has paid Anya's £3,000 into his account. State whether this is acceptable practice on Bradley's part.

(c) Anya owes Bradley £500 in fees.

(1) State whether he can he take the money owed to him out of the £3,000.

(2) If Bradley uses the money to pay his fees state **ONE** offence he might be accused of.

(d) State **ONE** circumstance when a professional accountant cannot hold money for a client.

Task 4

(a)   Explain whether the duty of confidentiality is more important to a professional accountant in practice or a professional accountant in business.

(b)   Sanjeev is a professional accountant who works as a sole practitioner. He suspects one of his clients, Pyrotech Ltd, is polluting a local river with toxic chemicals, which is illegal under the Environmental Protection Act.

    (1)   In this situation state whether he can disclose this confidential information.

    (2)   If Sanjeev decides to disclose this information explain **ONE** step he might take before doing so.

Tasks 5-9

Tasks 5-9 are based on the following project scenario and the six matters listed. Each task indicates which of the six specific matters is/are relevant to the task.

Project Scenario

Inkwell Limited is a family owned business that makes and sells ink for the printing industry. It employs 120 people. The factory is in Coventry, with two distribution sites in Bristol and Watford. The accounts department employs a qualified finance director, a qualified financial controller, two part-qualified student accountants and six assistants.

The accounts department uses an external payroll bureau and produces monthly management accounts, using computerised accounting software. The finance director produces year-end accounts and deals with all tax matters relating to the business.

You are George, one of the part-qualified accountants. You report to Janine, the financial controller.

Recently the following six matters have come to light.

Matter 1

Janine, the financial controller is away for two weeks on holiday and has forgotten to forward her emails to the finance director. The finance director has asked you to check her emails to see if there is anything that requires urgent attention. You find the following email:

Email
From :   Henry Bullet, Sales Director , Inkblot Ltd
To: Janine Hudgell, Financial Controller, Inkwell Ltd

Hi Janine,

I really enjoyed our chat over lunch in The Old Crown last week. I never realised my new sister-in-law worked in the same business as me! As you know, we are competing against Inkwell Ltd for a large printing contract. I understand you are looking at the pricing for this. Are you able to send a copy of Inkwell Ltd's tender to me, so I can make sure ours is lower? I realise this might be difficult for you but am happy to give you £2,000 for your time and effort. Might I suggest we meet in The Old Crown at the end of the month to complete the exchange?

Best wishes

Henry

Matter 2

George has noticed that a customer, Will & Harry Ltd, is spending around £250,000 on ink each year and paying in cash. The financial controller of Inkwell Ltd is a shareholder of Will & Harry Ltd.

Matter 3

The financial controller has recently been involved in considering tenders that Inkwell Ltd has received for a new integrated production and accounting system programme that is to be written specifically for the business. The tender process that has been followed is set out below:

- Only suppliers approved by the Board of Directors of Inkwell Ltd can be considered.

- Any relationships between suppliers and board members must be declared prior to a short list of suppliers being drawn up.

- All suppliers must be provided with the detailed specification and the decision criteria that Inkwell Ltd will use, as agreed by the Board.

- All tenders to be received by 31 July 20X3.

- The production director, finance director and managing director must assess all tenders against the specified decision criteria.

- The Board must approve and recommend the preferred supplier on 30 September 2013.

- The preferred supplier will be informed on 1 October 2013 and all other suppliers will be informed the next day that they have not been successful.

Matter 4

The finance director has recently reviewed the service provided by the payroll bureau. He has discovered that the bureau has recently made several mistakes and has concluded that it is becoming increasingly expensive to use. He has now decided that he would like to set up a payroll department at Inkwell Ltd and has selected an appropriate payroll software package. He has suggested that George should be responsible for producing the payroll and would like it to be up and running within three months. He has said that he will give George a promotion and a significant pay rise if he takes on this additional responsibility. He tells George that he is impressed with his 'can do' attitude and is 'sure he will pick it up quickly'. He would like a decision within three weeks.

George has no experience of running a payroll system and would prefer to become more involved in producing the management accounts. However, he has been hoping for promotion in the next few months.

Matter 5

George has asked the finance director for a copy of Inkwell Ltd's tax return, to help him in his accounting studies. Whilst reviewing it, he noticed that the amounts included for business entertaining do not agree with the figures in the general ledger, which means that the tax payable by the business was understated by £30,000. The tax computation has been agreed by HMRC. George has mentioned this to the finance director who refuses to raise the issue with either the Board of Directors or HMRC.

Matter 6

To enhance the company's reputation with customers, employees and suppliers, the directors of Inkwell Ltd feel it is appropriate for the company to consider how it can promote economic sustainability, as well as environmental and social sustainability but are not sure how to implement this.

Task 5

Refer to the Project Scenario and Matter 1.

(a) Explain which three of James's fundamental ethical principles are most threatened by the situation outlined in Henry Bullet's email.

(1)
(2)
(3)

(b) In terms of the conceptual framework, explain the two threats being faced by Janine.

(1)
(2)

Task 6

Refer to the Project Scenario and Matter 2 & 3

(a)   Explain whether George needs to take any action, including informing third parties, with respect to Will & Harry Ltd.

(b)   Explain how Inkwell Ltd's process for assessing tenders complies with the three elements of the Institute of Business Ethics simple three part ethical test.

(c)   Explain what type of operational risk the new integrated production and accounting programme could address.

Task 7

Refer to the Project Scenario and Matter 4

(a) Explain which **TWO** of George's fundamental ethical principles are most threatened by this situation.

(b) Explain the steps George must take to resolve this conflict of interest.

(c) Assume George now agrees to take on responsibility for producing the payroll. He realises that the mistakes made by the payroll bureau will lead to Inkwell Ltd incurring substantial fines if they are identified by HMRC. When George tells the finance director about this, he tells George to keep quiet. Explain what action George should take in relation to this conflict of loyalties.

Task 8

Refer to the Project Scenario and Matter 5

(a)   Explain the issue that the underpayment of tax raises for George and for Inkwell Ltd.

(b)   Explain what action should George take in this situation.

(c)   Explain who else George could discuss this situation with, whilst maintaining confidentiality at Inkwell Ltd, and the consequences for George.

(d)   If after taking all possible action without breaching confidentiality, Inkwell Ltd will not report the error, explain what action George must take.

Task 9

Refer to Matter 6

(a) **(1)** Explain what is meant by sustainable development, as set out in the Brundtland Report commissioned by the United Nations.

(2) Explain two of the three main elements of sustainability as defined in this report.

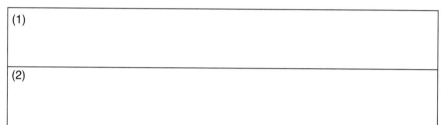

(1)

(2)

(b) Explain two actions Inkwell Ltd can take to support economic sustainability.

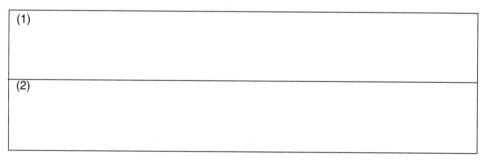

(1)

(2)

(c) Explain how the accountant's duty to society as a whole supports sustainability.

Practice assessment 2

Instructions to candidates

To 'state' something, you need to answer with a fact. If you are asked to 'explain' something you need to state the relevant fact and then give brief reason(s) for why that fact is the right answer. If you are asked to 'describe' you should set out what is involved without further explanation.

Task 1

(a) The body responsible for regulating the UK accountancy profession as a whole is abbreviated to FRC. What does FRC stand for?

(b) Global ethical standards for accountants are set by the International Ethics Standards Board for Accountants (IESBA). Which global body is this a part of?

(c) Name the four sponsoring bodies of AAT.

(1)
(2)
(3)
(4)

(d)   State two of the three statutory regulated (reserved) areas in accountancy and finance.

(1)
(2)

(e)   Accountants have five fundamental ethical principles with which they have a duty to comply. Explain whether this only applies to qualified professional accountants or whether it extends to student members of the professional accounting bodies.

Task 2

(a) State two of the three key ways in which a professional accountant can maintain his/her professional competence.

(1)
(2)

(b) Mitchell is a professional accountant with his own medium sized practice where he employs three additional members of staff. He prepares sets of final accounts and tax returns for a wide range of sole traders and partnerships.

Given Mitchell's client base, explain **TWO** areas of technical knowledge in which Mitchell must keep up-to-date.

(c) Complete the following statement:

A professional accountant who keeps him/herself up-to-date with developments in the accounting profession, and takes the appropriate amount of care to ensure that the quality of the work performed meets the high standards expected of the accounting profession, has complied with the fundamental ethical principle of... .

(d)   Elouise, a professional accountant in practice, has acted outside the limits of her professional expertise during an assignment for Phillip. Phillip has incurred substantial additional bank interest and charges as a result.

State two grounds on which Phillip may be able to seek compensation from Elouise for these costs.

(1)
(2)

(e)   Daphne is a professional accountant in practice. Her client, Florence, has applied for the lease on a new shop on the high street. The landlord of the new premises has asked Daphne to provide some financial information about Florence together with a written reference confirming Florence will be able to pay the rent on the shop for the term of the lease.

(1)   Explain whether Daphne can provide the financial information to the landlord.

(2)   Is it acceptable for Daphne to include a disclaimer of liability in the written reference?

(3)   If Daphne gives the reference, even though she knows Florence will struggle to pay the rent, what kind of fraud is she committing?

(f)   Sally is a professional accountant who works as a sole-trader. She has been asked to give her opinion on the way in which one of her clients, Maxima Ltd, has calculated the depreciation for its plant and machinery. She has given her opinion despite being aware that she did not have sufficient information on which to base it.

In addition to integrity, explain which other **ONE** of Sally's fundamental ethical principles is threatened by this situation.

Task 3

Vincent is a professional accountant in practice. His client, Nicky, has asked Vincent to hold £7,300 for her until it is due to be paid to her landlord for her quarterly rent. Nicky has given Vincent the money in cash and is refusing to say where it has come from. Vincent is concerned that the money may be criminal property.

(a)   With what crime could Vincent be charged if he retains Nicky's money without notifying the authorities?

(b)   Nicky has now provided Vincent with sufficient evidence that the money is not criminal property and Vincent has agreed to hold the money for her until it is due to be paid to the landlord.

    (1)   Complete the following sentence:

        'Vincent is holding the money in .... for Nicky and therefore acting

        as a ....'.

    (2)   Can Vincent use the money to improve his cash flow in the business provided he ensures that it is available to pay Nicky's landlord when the rent falls due?

    (3)   If Vincent does not properly account for the client monies give **ONE** of the two crimes that he could be charged with.

Task 4

(a)   Confidentiality is one of the five fundamental ethical principles that a professional accountant is expected to adhere to.

Complete the following sentence:

'In addition to being an ethical principle, confidentiality is also a .... obligation.'

(b)   Desmond currently works for Thompson and Groves, a successful firm of accountants in Middletown. He has recently been offered a job with Parkes & Co. Before Desmond accepts the job he asks for a meeting with Edward Parkes, the managing partner at Parkes & Co. At the meeting Desmond offers to provide Parkes & Co with details of the works that he carried out for his clients at Thompson and Groves. Explain whether Desmond can use knowledge, information and experience gained from a previous employer in a new job.

(c)   Mary-Beth is a professional accountant in practice. As part of her work for her client, Aisha, Mary-Beth has obtained confidential information.

Give two circumstances in which it would be appropriate for Mary-Beth to disclose this confidential information:

(1)
(2)

Tasks 5-9

Tasks 5-9 are based on the following project scenario and the six matters listed. Each task indicates which of the six specific matters is/are relevant to the task.

Project Scenario

Pitkin & Co is a medium sized accounting practice in Bettertown. Pitkin & Co employs 12 fully qualified professional accountants, five part-qualified student accountants and seven administrative staff.

Sandra is the office manager who manages the team of administrative staff. Her first job each morning is to open all post received. Once opened the post is then replaced in its envelope and placed in the relevant person's pigeonhole for him/her to collect.

Pitkin & Co's clients include:

·   Ambridge Ltd, a delivery company run by Edward Coll

·   Matthews Ltd, a small plumbing business with annual revenue of £110,000

·   Bolt Supplies Ltd, a company which provides golf equipment to golf clubs and sport shops throughout the area

·   Mendel Ltd and Bryce Ltd, both of which are recruitment companies based in Bettertown

·   Wittenbury Travel Ltd, a new client which operates as a travel agent

·   Rosslyn Organics Ltd, a new client which sells organic and Fairtrade products to businesses in the catering industry.

You are Jordan, one of the five part-qualified student accountants at Pitkin & Co. You report to Cyril, one of the junior managers who is a qualified professional accountant.

Recently the following six matters have come to light.

Matter 1

Eli Keszler, one of the newly qualified accountants in Pitkin & Co, has been on holiday for the last week. Sandra, the office manager, has asked you whether anyone is checking the post in Eli's pigeonhole as it's getting quite full. Normally Cyril would check his colleague's post but he is out of the office until tomorrow so Sandra tells you to go through Eli's pigeonhole to see if there is anything that needs to be dealt with urgently. You have found the following letter:

Letter from: Edward Coll, Ambridge Ltd

To: Eli Keszler, Pitkin & Co

Dear Eli,

I am very concerned that you appear to be ignoring my emails. I have sent you several now and am considering calling the office to discuss your client care. I wonder what George Pitkin would say if I told him about our arrangement. I need to put my bid in for providing the delivery services to Bolt Supplies Ltd by the end of this week. If you don't send me the information you promised about what it currently pays its existing delivery company then I can't make sure my company's bid is lower. I know you're worried about providing me with confidential information about another of your clients, but this arrangement benefits us all. Bolt Supplies Ltd gets high quality delivery services at a very competitive price, Pitkin & Co continues to have my business and you get the £1,000 I promised you for helping me.

Please get back to me as soon as possible.

Kind regards,

Edward

Matter 2

William Matthews, the owner of Matthews Ltd, a small plumbing business, has contacted Pitkin & Co. He has asked for some help in applying for a bank loan to purchase a beauty salon which his wife, Christina, is hoping to open in Bettertown. The loan is for £250,000.

Matter 3

Bolt Supplies Ltd has produced a draft Code of Practice for use within its accounting and payroll department. Although there are several qualified accountants who work in this department of Bolt Supplies Ltd they are keen to have an independent review from Pitkin & Co. You have been handed the following extract:

Confidential

Extract from the draft Code of Practice for the accounting and payroll department of Bolt Supplies Ltd

This Code of Practice is for use by the accounting and payroll staff only.

All members of the accounting and payroll staff at Bolt Supplies Ltd will aim to ensure that:

a)   Requests for information from regulators, other departments, customers or suppliers will be dealt with in a timely manner and with openness, honesty, accuracy and respect.

b)   Personal information held in the accounting and payroll department will be handled sensitively and with respect and in accordance with the data protection act and other relevant statutory requirements.

c)   If a complaint is raised by the supplier all prices paid to suppliers will be reviewed by a senior person for their fairness to both parties.

d)   Suppliers will be paid within 30 days of the end of the month in which the invoice is received, unless the supplier's terms differ from this.

e)   No staff member in the department will accept a gift or hospitality from any individual or organisation with whom the business deals unless (a) its worth is less than £40 AND (b) the offer is routinely made in the normal course of the individual/organisation's business to other business associates.

f)   If the department receives a complaint from an employee regarding the amount or timing of a salary or expense payment he/she will receive a response within 2 working days.

Matter 4

Pitkin & Co have several clients that are recruitment businesses. Reginald is Pitkin & Co's specialist in preparing accounts and providing advice to this type of business. Two of its clients in this industry, Mendel Ltd and Bryce Ltd, are both tendering for the exclusive contract to provide staff to the local authority in Bettertown. Each client has asked Reginald to provide them with advice on its tender document. When Mendel Ltd realises that Bryce Ltd is also tendering for the local authority contract it offers Pitkin & Co an extra £5,000 to act for it exclusively. Bryce Ltd would also like Reginald's exclusive advice and has offered Pitkin & Co an additional £6,000 for this.

Matter 5

Pitkin & Co have recently started an engagement for a new client, Wittenbury Travel Ltd, a large travel agency that has recently relocated to Bettertown. As with all its new clients, Pitkin & Co followed its prescribed customer due diligence procedures prior to taking on Wittenbury Travel Ltd as a client. Libby, one of Pitkin & Co's qualified professional accountants, had been working at Wittenbury Travel Ltd's premises for the past week and has been very concerned about a number of transactions that she has discovered relating to overseas flights. All these sales have been made for cash and the passengers' names have not been recorded. The total of these sales is over £20,000.

Libby has asked the managing director of Wittenbury Travel Ltd for more details relating to these transactions but he has refused to give it to her. Libby now believes that her client may be involved in terrorist financing.

Matter 6

One of Pitkin & Co's newest clients, Rosslyn Organics Ltd has recently contacted Cyril to discuss Pitkin & Co's attitude to sustainability and sustainable development. They have explained to him that as part of their CSR they only trade with businesses that can prove they are keen to promote sustainability and sustainable development. They have asked Cyril to provide them with evidence that Pitkin & Co encourages all its clients to focus on their 'triple bottom line when measuring their performance'.

Task 5

Refer to the Project Scenario and Matter 1.

(a) Explain which **THREE** of Eli Keszler's fundamental ethical principles are being most threatened by the points raised in Edward Coll's letter.

(b) What are the two threats to his fundamental ethical principles being faced by Eli?

(1)
(2)

Task 6

Refer to the Project Scenario and Matters 2 and 3.

(a) Explain why customer due diligence (CDD) procedures should be carried out by Pitkin & Co with respect to William Matthews' request to help with the application for a bank loan.

(b) Explain Bolt Supplies Ltd's five key ethical organisational values with reference to this draft Code of Practice.

(1)
(2)
(3)
(4)
(5)

(c) If a member of the accounting and payroll department staff at Bolt Supplies Ltd fails to comply with the Code of Practice once it has been implemented, explain whether he/she could face legal action from the business for failure to comply.

Task 7

Refer to the Project Scenario and Matter 4.

(a)   Explain which two of Reginald's fundamental ethical principles are threatened by the fact that both Mendel Ltd and Bryce Ltd are tendering for the local authority contract.

(1)
(2)

(b)   Explain the process Reginald should go through to resolve the ethical conflict that he faces when deciding how to act in respect of this matter.

(c)   Assuming that Reginald decides he can act for one of the clients, answer the following questions:

   (1)   Explain whether he should choose to act for Bryce Ltd simply because it has offered a higher fee.

   (2)   Explain what safeguards Reginald should put in place before carrying out the engagement for the client he chooses to act for.

Task 8

Refer to the Project Scenario and Matter 5.

(a)   Explain the actions that Libby must take in respect of her concerns relating to Wittenbury Travel Ltd.

(b)   Explain whether or not Libby should discuss her concerns with the managing director of Wittenbury Travel Ltd.

(c)   Explain what consequences Libby may face if she does not take any action in relation to her concerns about the possible terrorist financing.

Task 9

Refer to the Project Scenario and Matter 6.

(a)   What does the abbreviation CSR stand for in relation to the enquiry by Rosslyn Organics Ltd?

(b)   Explain the professional accountant's obligation to uphold the values of sustainability.

(c)

(1)   Explain what Rosslyn Organics Ltd means by the phrase 'triple bottom line'.

(2)   For each of the factors identified in c(1) give **ONE** example of a way in which Pitkin & Co itself can take action to encourage sustainability in the way it operates its own business.

Practice
assessment 3

Instructions to candidates

To 'state' something, you need to answer with a fact. If you are asked to 'explain' something you need to state the relevant fact and then give brief reason(s) for why that fact is the right answer. If you are asked to 'describe' you should set out what is involved without further explanation.

Task 1

(a) Which UK body is responsible for setting standards for corporate reporting, and oversees the regulatory activities of the UK professional accounting bodies?

(b) What is the name of the body responsible for regulating financial services in the UK?

(c) Which professional accounting body is a sponsoring body of the AAT but is not a member of the Consultative Committee of Accounting Bodies (CCAB)?

(d) State the three statutory regulated functions (reserved areas) of work that an accountant carries out.

(1)
(2)
(3)

Task 2

(a) A professional accountant has taken a year out to go travelling around the world. He is due to return to work at a small accounting practice shortly. State what fundamental ethical principle is most threatened by the fact that he has spent a year away from work?

(b) Jamie is an employed accountant who assists the finance director in the production of year-end accounts for several companies in the corporate group for which he works.

Explain the key area of technical knowledge that is critical to Jamie's role.

(c) Riley is a newly qualified professional accountant who works for Brightings Ltd, a business that produces industrial lighting. He has been asked by the finance director to prepare the year-end information for the external auditors relating to non-current assets. The finance director is unable to do this work as she is renegotiating a bank loan. Previously Riley has only ever carried out depreciation calculations at college, and the schedules that are required for Brightings Ltd are complicated. The finance director has mentioned that Riley's pay review is due next month and that she will take into account how well he carries out this work as part of this review.

(1) Explain which of Riley's fundamental ethical principles is being most threatened in this situation.

(2) Explain two safeguards that could be put in place to address this threat.

(1)
(2)

(d) Marisa is a part qualified professional accountant who works for Whykea Ltd, a furniture manufacturing business. One of the business's customers has contacted her and asked if she could date a number of its March invoices as having been issued in February. The customer's year-end is February and it is keen to reduce its tax bill.

(1) Which of Marisa's fundamental ethical principles is most threatened by this situation?

(2) Explain what action she should take.

Task 3

Pasha is a professional accountant who works in a large accountancy practice. He has been approached by Fine Builders Ltd to provide them with some tax advice. They have asked him to hold £40,000 to pay the tax when it falls due. They will pay the money to Pasha in cash.

(a) Explain what procedures Pasha must carry out before he can hold this money for Fine Builders Ltd.

(b) If after carrying out the procedures identified in (a) above Pasha decides he can hold the money, state in what capacity he would be holding the money for Fine Builders Ltd.

(c) If Pasha invests the money in a high interest bearing account until it is needed, answer the following:

(1) State who is entitled to the interest earned on the balance.

(2) Pasha wants to use the interest to pay his fees. State whether he can do this.

Task 4

(a) Geoffrey is a professional accountant in practice who works for a medium sized firm. His client, Gurinder, believes that any confidential information he shares with Geoffrey cannot be disclosed to anyone else under any circumstances.

(1) State whether this is true or false.

---

(2) State what statute (law) protects information that Geoffrey holds about Gurinder and state the name of the office which enforces the provisions of this statute.

(b) Gurinder is currently in dispute with his landlord over unpaid rent. The matter is now going to court and the landlord has asked Geoffrey for copies of Gurinder's bank statements. In this situation explain what Geoffrey should do.

Tasks 5-9

Tasks 5-9 are based on the following project scenario and the six matters listed. Each task indicates which of the six specific matters is/are relevant to the task.

Project Scenario

Frances, Philips and Nightingale are a firm of accountants, providing accounting and taxation services to a range of clients. They employ several qualified accountants, four part-qualified accountants and two clerical/ administrative staff.

They have a range of clients, including the following:

- Sam's Hairdressing Salons, a chain of hairdressing salons which has been a client for a number of years

- James Blandon, a new client who is a personal trainer, with annual profits of £30,000

- The Waterhole Ltd, a new client that runs a chain of bars, with an annual turnover of £600,000

- The Growing Business, an independent garden centre that has been a client for several years. Its turnover over is £300,000 per annum

- Greenshoots nursery, a new client with an annual turnover of over £100,000

- Chicago Diner Ltd, a chain of ten restaurants based throughout the Midlands

- Partywares Ltd, an established client that manufactures paper-based party products

You are Hannah Wright, one of the part-qualified accountants who works for Frances, Philips and Nightingale.

Matter 1

You have received in error an email from a client, Sam's Hairdressing Salons that was meant for Henry Wright, another part-qualified accountant.

Email
To: H Wright, Frances, Philips and Nightingale
From : Sam Packham, Sam's Hairdressing Salons
Hi Henry,

Thank you so much for your help with the business plan. The bank is really happy with the plan and has finally approved that loan we applied for to finance our expansion. I am now keen to recruit a new accountant and would like you to consider the position. The new accountant would be responsible for producing all relevant financial information required by the bank, as well as sourcing and implementing any new systems we need to cope with the expansion of the business.

I am also hoping that a friend of mine, Vanessa, will invest in the business. I would be really grateful if you could talk her through the business plan and explain what a good investment it would be for her.

Perhaps we can discuss this when you come next week to prepare our year-end accounts.

Best wishes

Sam

Matter 2

You have been working closely with Alex Boyd, one of the qualified accountants. You have noticed that there has been no customer due diligence documentation (CDD) carried out on two new clients, James Blandon, a personal trainer, and The Waterhole Ltd, a chain of bars. When you raised this with Alex, he said that he had been too busy to do it and both clients needed the assignments to be done quickly. Alex added that one of the partners, Ken Nightingale, had told him not to worry about it, as it is 'only a bit of paperwork'.

Matter 3

You have recently been asked to look after Matthew, who is with Frances, Philips and Nightingale for a month's work experience. As part of his introduction to the firm he was given the written Code of Practice to read which details how staff should deal with employees, clients and suppliers. He is unclear as to the purpose of the code.

The Code of Practice is set out below:

Frances, Philips and Nightingale

Code of Practice – Finance Department

1. Information requested by individuals or organisations will be produced promptly and accurately. Staff will be honest, open and respectful when dealing with individuals or organisations.

2. Information held about individuals will comply with all relevant statutory requirements.

3. Purchases of supplies will be at a fair price.

4. Suppliers will be paid promptly to agreed terms.

5. Gifts from clients or suppliers of £20 or under can be accepted, as long as the offer is made to the majority of employees at Frances Philips and Nightingale. Gifts over £20 may not be accepted.

6. Staff salary and expense payments will be made in accordance with the issued timetable. Any complaints regarding pay or expense amounts will be considered and replied to within 24 hours of receipt into the finance department.

7. All staff will have an annual performance review where members of staff will receive feedback on their performance over the year and an explanation of their salary for the following year. Training requests will be discussed at this meeting and financial support by the practice for the costs of training will be considered.

Matter 4

Magda, one of the qualified professional accountants at Frances, Philips and Nightingale has worked for several years with a client, The Growing Business; an independent garden centre. Magda has just been given responsibility for a new client, Greenshoots nursery that is owned by Steve. He has offered to give Magda £1,000 if she will help him falsely reduce the tax payable on the previous year's trading.

The Growing Business has identified Greenshoots nursery as a potential acquisition. It has asked Magda to help with the acquisition process, including negotiating the price that it will pay Steve for the business. It has said that, should the acquisition be successful Frances, Philips and Nightingale will benefit from having a much larger client.

Magda is aware that Greenshoots nursery is currently having financial difficulties and that Steve may be prepared to accept a lower price for the business than The Growing Business realise.

Matter 5

Lisa is one of the qualified accountants working for Frances, Philips and Nightingale. She is currently producing the tax return for Chicago Diner Ltd, a chain of ten American-themed restaurants. It has been a client for several years however, the accountant who produced the previous year's return has now left Frances, Philips and Nightingale. While Lisa is preparing the return, she realises that the income from one of the restaurants in the chain was not included in the figures used for previous year's return. However, all the restaurant's expenses were included. This has resulted in the tax liability for the previous year being significantly less than it should have been. When Lisa brings this to the attention of the directors of Chicago Diner Ltd they tell her to prepare the return correctly this year but refuse to amend the previous year's return.

Matter 6

You are currently working on the accounts of Partywares Ltd, a company that manufactures paper decorations, tablecloths and napkins. The directors have decided to review all the business's suppliers to ensure that they are obtaining sustainably sourced paper. This is one of their objectives that they set in the organisation's Corporate Social Responsibility Report and they are keen to achieve this aim. They would like to include this report in their financial statements which Frances, Philips and Nightingale produce.

Task 5

Refer to the Project Scenario and Matter 1

(a) Explain which three of Henry Wright's fundamental ethical principles are most threatened by the situation outlined in Sam Packham's email.

(1)
(2)
(3)

(b) In terms of the conceptual framework, explain the two threats to his fundamental ethical principles being faced by Henry.

(1)
(2)

Task 6

Refer to the Project Scenario and Matter 2 & 3

(a) Explain why accountants carry out customer due diligence (CDD) procedures for new clients.

(b) Explain why Ken Nightingale's comment regarding the need for CDD has influenced Alex not to perform customer due diligence.

(c) If Alex fails to carry out CDD, explain what type of misconduct his professional accounting body may discipline him for.

(d) State the most severe penalty that Alex could face if disciplined by his professional accounting body.

```



```

(e) Identify for Matthew three of Frances, Philips and Nightingale's key ethical organisational values with reference to its Code of Practice. You should identify the points in the Code of Practice that address each of the ethical values you identify.

(1)

(2)

(3)

(f) Explain to Matthew why the code exists and whether the code is enforceable in law or not.

```



```

Task 7

Refer to the Project Scenario and Matter 4

(a)   State what this offer of payment constitutes and what offence Steve could be charged with for making this offer.

(b)   Explain which two of Magda's fundamental ethical principles are threatened by The Growing Business wanting to acquire Greenshoots nursery?

(1)

(2)

(c)   Explain two actions Magda could take to resolve this conflict.

(1)

(2)

Task 8

Refer to the Project Scenario and Matter 5

(a) Explain whether Lisa can continue to act for Chicago Diners Ltd.

(b) **(1)** State who Lisa should then report her findings to.

(2) Identify two pieces of information she will need to disclose to them.

(1)

(2)

(c) Explain the consequences for Lisa if she does not report her findings.

Task 9

Refer to Matter 6

(a) State whether the directors of Partywares Ltd are legally required to produce a Corporate Social Responsibility Report?

(b) In relation to sustainability and sustainable development explain the **THREE** elements of the 'triple bottom line' that may be included in a CSR report.

(c) State three actions Partywares Ltd can take to support sustainability.

(1)
(2)
(3)

Practice
assessment 1
answers

Task 1

(a) International Federation of Accountants (IFAC)

(b) Serious Organised Crime Agency (SOCA)

(c) Two of:

Codes and Standards Committee, Conduct Committee and Executive Committee

(d) Two of: ICAEW, ICAS, ICAI, ACCA and CIPFA

(e) Civil law results in a claim in a civil court by a claimant against a defendant to enforce rights that arose between them (under contract, negligence and trust laws); there is no involvement by the state. The consequence is not punishment of the party who loses but some form of compensation for the party who wins.

Criminal law results in a prosecution in a criminal court by the state of the accused for a breach of the law, such as for the crimes of theft, money laundering, terrorist financing, bribery and fraud. The consequence is punishment of the accused, if found guilty, by imprisonment or fine.

Task 2

(a) At least twice in a twelve month period.

(b) Integrity

(c) **(1)** No

(2) Self-interest threat to Charlie's objectivity. As a professional accountant he should not have an interest – own shares or have loans – either directly or indirectly in a client he works on.

(3) If Susanne invests in Finley Ltd, Charlie should stop working for Finley Ltd.

(d) **(1)** Professional competence and due care

(2) Nikki is not competent to complete the tax return without supervision, so she should do one of the following:

- Ask her manager if she can observe him completing a similar tax return.

- Request for her manager to review the tax return, once complete, to make sure she has completed it correctly, prior to it being sent to the client.

- Discuss the situation with a colleague, who may be able to assist her in completing the tax return.

She must not complete and send out the tax return before a more experienced member of staff has reviewed it.

Task 3

(a)   Customer Due Diligence (CDD)

(b)   No

(c)   (1)   No

        (2)   One of: fraud by abuse of position, theft, breach of contract

(d)   One of

- Where the accountant suspects the money is derived from criminal activity.
- Where the money does not relate to a service that the accountant offers.
- Where the professional licence of the accountant in practice does not allow them to hold money on behalf of the client.

Task 4

(a)   It is equally important for a professional accountant in business and a professional accountant in practice to comply with the fundamental ethical principle of confidentiality. Both may learn confidential information about clients, customers and suppliers in the course of their work, which they have a duty to keep confidential.

(b)   (1)   Yes

        (2)   One of: contact his professional accounting body's advice line, seek legal advice

Task 5

(a)   Confidentiality – the tender information is confidential and very sensitive and so should not be shared with anyone outside the business.

        Objectivity – the offer of payment is allowing a conflict of interest to override Janine's professional judgement.

        Integrity – this is a bribe and therefore, dishonest.

(b)   Self-interest threat– Janine will benefit financially if she provides Henry with the information.

        Familiarity threat– Janine is related to Henry (sister-in-law) and so may not wish to upset him.

Task 6

(a)   It is unusual for a business to pay such large sums of cash for supplies. This may indicate that the cash has been illegally obtained. If this is the case it would mean that Inkwell Ltd could also be guilty of money laundering by accepting the cash payments.

        As the financial controller of Inkwell Ltd is a shareholder of Will & Harry Ltd, George should report his suspicions to the finance director. However, if he believes that the finance director is compliant with the arrangement then he should seek advice from his professional accounting body.

        George should report his suspicions to the Serious Organised Crime Agency (SOCA) using suspicious activity report (SAR).

(b) Transparent – the decision criteria is set out in the tender document. Any relationship that a director of Inkwell Ltd has with a supplier is declared prior to the tenders being considered.

Effect – the decision affects the production and accounts teams, who are represented in the assessment process by the production director and the finance director. The successful tender is based on detailed criteria.

Fairness – all suppliers have the same information and have access to the decision criteria that are used to assess the tenders.

(c) Systems risk – strong controls within the system should minimise the risk of loss to the business.

Task 7

(a) Professional competence and due care: George does not have the necessary experience to be able to produce the payroll for the business.

Objectivity: it is difficult to refuse a promotion, as George does not want to disappoint the finance director even if it is not in line with his long-term goals.

(b)
- Gather all the relevant information relating to the issue before making a decision.
- Discuss the position with the financial controller when she returns from her holiday.
- Discuss the issue with the finance director and explain that he does not feel he currently has the relevant experience to take on the role.
- Establish what training is available to him to become sufficiently competent to run the payroll system and what support he would be given during this time.
- Document any discussions and highlight the ethical issues that are involved and the consequences of each option.

(c) George is employed by Inkwell Ltd and does not want them to incur fines. However, he has an ethical duty as a professional accountant to comply with the law. He knows the payroll is incorrect and that as a consequence Inkwell Ltd is breaking the law.

He should encourage the finance director and other directors to report the issue to HMRC and correct the errors. If they are not willing to do so, George should contact his professional accounting body's advice line and if necessary take legal advice. If this does not resolve the issue then George may have to consider resigning. If he does this, he should clearly state the reasons for his resignation to management.

Task 8

(a) The unpaid tax means that Inkwell is retaining funds that have been obtained dishonestly. This now becomes criminal property and as a consequence Inkwell Ltd could be guilty of money laundering.

(b) He must try and persuade the finance director to report the error to HMRC and to pay the tax that is due.

(c) George could raise the issue with another member of Inkwell Ltd's Board of Directors. However, by doing this he is highlighting the finance director's unethical behaviour, so he could also contact his professional accounting body's advice line.

(d)   If George believes Inkwell Ltd is money laundering he must make a suspicious activity report to the Serious Organised Crime Agency (SOCA). Provided George makes the required disclosure to SOCA he will be protected from a claim for breach of confidentiality, as this will be a protected disclosure.

Task 9

(a)   **(1)**   'Development that meets the needs of the present without compromising the ability of future generations to meet their own needs.'

   (2)   Two of:

   Economic growth and sustainability: a business or a country will increase profits but not at the expense of society, employees or the environment.

   Social equality and sustainability: the organisation focuses on the wellbeing of employees and the communities and societies they belong to and affect.

   Environmental protection and sustainability: the environment is protected and preserved for future generations.

(b)   Two of:

   ·   Following a 'fair' pricing strategy with the customer, not charging whatever the customer can afford.

   ·   Paying suppliers to agreed terms.

   ·   Setting wage rates that reflect workers' skills and qualifications.

   ·   Consider the implications of financial decisions on society and the environment as well as on profits.

   Note: other reasonable answers would be acceptable for this task

(c)   Professional accountants have public interest duties to protect society as a whole, which means they must consider the economic, social and environmental aspects of their work and ensure long-term responsible management of resources used by their organisation.

Practice
assessment 2
answers

Task 1

    (a)   The Financial Reporting Council

    (b)   International Federation of Accountants (IFAC).

    (c)   ICAEW, CIMA, CIPFA and ICAS.

    (d)   Any two of: Audit, investment business or insolvency.

    (e)   All members of the professional accounting bodies including student and full members should comply with the fundamental ethical principles of the accounting profession.

Task 2

    (a)   Any two of: reading professional journals, attending updating courses or complying with CPD requirements.

    (b)   Identify two of: accounting regulations; tax legislation; money laundering regulations; accounting and reporting standards.

           These areas are important for sole traders and partnerships because these types of clients must produce accurate accounts and tax returns. Mitchell must also protect himself from the threats associated with a client being engaged in money laundering.

    (c)   A professional accountant who keeps him/herself up-to-date with developments in the accounting profession, and takes the appropriate amount of care to ensure that the quality of the work performed meets the high standards expected of the accounting profession has complied with the fundamental ethical principle of **professional competence and due care**.

    (d)   **(1)**   An action for breach of contract.

           (2)   An action for professional negligence.

    (e)   **(1)**   Daphne must obtain authorisation from Florence before she can provide the financial information that the landlord has requested.

           (2)   Yes

           (3)   Fraud by false representation.

    (f)   Professional competence and due care. Sally is basing her opinion on inadequate information and so is not acting in accordance with applicable professional standards or with due care.

Task 3

    (a)   Money laundering.

    (b)   **(1)**   'Vincent is holding the money in **trust** for Nicky and therefore acting as a **trustee**.'

           (2)   No, the money that Vincent is holding for Nicky must be held in a separate client bank account until it is due to be paid to Nicky's landlord.

           (3)   Either of theft or fraud by abuse of position.

Task 4

(a)   'In addition to being an ethical principle, confidentiality is also a **legal** obligation.'

(b)   Desmond is allowed to use general knowledge and experience from a previous employer but NOT specific information from that employer that is covered by the duty of confidentiality.

(c)   Any two of the following:

- when Mary-Beth is authorised by Aisha to disclose the confidential information
- when Mary-Beth is required by law to disclose the confidential information
- when Mary-Beth has a professional duty to disclose the information

Task 5

(a)   The three fundamental principles most threatened are:

Confidentiality – providing the information that Edward is asking for about Bolt Supplies Ltd is breaching Eli's duty of client confidentiality.

Objectivity – if Eli gives in to the pressure being put on him by Edward and the offer of payment this will compromise Eli's professional judgement and hence his objectivity.

Professional behaviour – providing confidential information to Edward is in breach of Eli's duty of confidentiality and therefore, brings the accounting profession into disrepute.

(b)   Self-interest threat from Edwards's offer of cash in return for the confidential information.

Intimidation threat from Edward's comment that he 'wonders what George Pitkin would say if he found out about their arrangement'.

Task 6

(a)   CDD should be carried out because:

- Although Matthews Ltd is an existing client of Pitkin & Co, the purchase of a beauty salon is inconsistent with prior knowledge of the client and with the client's normal business.
- The salon will be managed by Christina, William's wife, who is not a client of Pitkin & Co.

(b)
- Report financial and regulatory information clearly and on time (covered by point a)
- Be transparent with colleagues, customers and suppliers (covered by point a)
- Be open and honest by identifying when it is appropriate to accept gifts and hospitality (covered by point e)
- Pay suppliers a fair price and on time (covered by points c and d)
- Provide fair treatment to employees (covered by points b and f)

(c)   This Code of Practice is voluntary and has been prepared by Bolt Supplies Ltd for its own use; it has not been created by statutory legislation. This means that a member of staff who fails to comply with the Code of Practice would not face legal action.

Task 7

(a)   •   Confidentiality – Reginald has confidential information about both Mendel Ltd and Bryce Ltd.

   •   Objectivity – there is a conflict of interest between Mendel Ltd and Bryce Ltd. Even if Reginald is able to remain independent when acting for both clients he must also appear to be independent. This means that any reasonable person should be confident that he is behaving independently. In this situation it is difficult to act without a perception of bias when there is such a conflict of interests between the two clients.

(b)   The ethical conflict resolution process that Reginald should go through is:

   •   consider relevant facts and the ethical issues involved and how they affect his ability to comply with his fundamental ethical principles

   •   apply any established procedures for ethical conflict resolution that Pitkin & Co already have in place

   •   establish all the alternative courses of action that are available to him

   •   for each of these options establish which is most consistent with the fundamental principles and determine the consequences of each

   •   speak to a more senior member of staff art Pitkin & Co and ask his/her advice

   •   document the full ethical conflict resolution process that he has followed including the issues, options and discussions

   •   if he cannot resolve the ethical conflict he should seek advice from his professional accounting body

(c)   **(1)**   Reginald should not simply choose to act for the client that has offered the highest fees. Instead he must consider which client he can act for without compromising his fundamental ethical principles. If there is no increased risk with either of the clients then he can choose to act for Bryce Ltd.

   (2)   Reginald must consider implementing appropriate safeguards so that his familiarity with the other client does not affect his objectivity and so that he does not breach the duty of client confidentiality that he has to the other client. This may be best achieved by Reginald no longer working on the client that he decides not to act for during the tender process.

Task 8

(a)   Libby must make an internal report to Pitkin & Co's Money Laundering Reporting Officer (MLRO) detailing her suspicions. She must also inform Wittenbury Travel Ltd that Pitkin & Co can no longer act for it.

(b)   Libby should not discuss her concerns with the managing director of Wittenbury Travel Ltd as this could result in her being guilty of the offence of 'tipping off'.

(c)   If Libby takes no action in relation to her concerns and continues to act for Wittenbury Travel Ltd and it is found to be involved in terrorist financing she will also be guilty of terrorist financing. As Pitkin & Co is a firm in the regulated sector, failure to take the appropriate action under the Proceeds of Crime Act will mean that Libby has committed the crime of failure to disclose.

Task 9

(a)   Corporate Social Responsibility

(b)   Professional accountants have a responsibility to act in the public interest. This includes supporting sustainability and sustainable development and considering the risks to society as a whole in not acting sustainably.

(c)   (1)   This relates to the three factors highlighted in the Brundtland report and expects Pitkin & Co to encourage its clients to take economic, environmental and social factors into account when measuring their position and performance and when it make short and long-term decisions.

(2)   An example is given for each of the three factors; however any reasonable answer for each would be acceptable.

Economic – Pitkin & Co should, where possible, source goods and services from local suppliers within Bettertown.

Environmental – Pitkin & Co could introduce recycling policies throughout the organisation for paper, plastic and other consumables.

Social – Pitkin & Co could encourage all staff to take part in local charitable activities and provide them with time off work, or financial support to do so.

Practice assessment 3 answers

Task 1

(a)   Financial Reporting Council

(b)   Financial Conduct Authority

(c)   CIMA

(d)   ·   external audit

·   investment business

·   insolvency

Task 2

(a)   Professional competence and due care

(b)   Changes in financial reporting standards, as he needs this to ensure the year-end accounts comply with current standards

(c)   **(1)**   Professional competence and due care.   He does not currently have sufficient experience to complete the work unsupervised, and so there may be a risk that it will not produce the information to a satisfactory standard.

(2)   ·   Obtain advice or training from a colleague in the department on how to complete the information

·   Ensure he has sufficient time to complete the work

·   Discuss the situation with a senior member of staff

·   Contact his professional accounting body for advice

(d)   **(1)**   Integrity – If Marisa does this she will be acting dishonestly as she knows the customer is trying to reduce its tax bill dishonestly.

(2)   ·   She should explain to the customer that she is not able to do this.

·   She should inform a more senior member of the accounts department what has happened.

·   She should document the issue, so the person who handles the customer's account will be aware of what has happened, should the customer complain in the future.

Task 3

(a)   As Fine Builders Ltd is a potential new client, Pasha must carry out customer due diligence (CDD) before he can hold this money for it.

(b)   As a trustee

(c)   **(1)**   Fine Builders Ltd

(2)   No

Task 4

   (a)   **(1)**   False

            (2)   •   Data Protection Act 1998
                    •   Information Commissioner's Office

   (b)   Geoffrey has a duty of confidentiality to his client, Gurinder and so is not permitted to disclose the information to the landlord. Geoffrey could request authorisation from Gurinder to disclose the information to his landlord, although in these circumstances it is unlikely that this permission will be given.

            If a court order is issued requiring that Geoffrey provides the bank statements, then he must comply with this.

Task 5

   (a)   Professional competence and due care – as Henry is not yet fully qualified it is unlikely he will have the necessary skills and experience to source and implement new systems and to produce all the financial information the bank will want.

            Objectivity – Henry has been offered a job by a client. This could compromise his professional judgement when producing the year-end accounts.

            Professional behaviour – if Henry accepts a job he knows he is not qualified or competent to do, he could bring the reputation of the accounting profession into disrepute.

   (b)   Self-interest – the offer of employment by Sam's Hairdressing Salons could create financial interest in the business for Henry.

            Advocacy threat – by recommending the business to Vanessa as an investment, Henry is promoting the business and faces an advocacy threat to his objectivity.

Task 6

   (a)   Customer due diligence (CDD) is carried out on new clients to ensure that the client is not engaged in money laundering and to ensure that any monies the accountant deals with are not proceeds of crime.

   (b)   Ken is a partner in Frances, Philips and Nightingale. He therefore sets an example to the rest of the staff that work for the firm. The 'tone at the top' will influence their attitude to ethical behaviour. In this case Ken does not see the importance of CDD which will influence Alex to have the same attitude.

   (c)   Alex could be disciplined for bringing the profession into disrepute, as he broke the law by not following Money Laundering Regulations.

   (d)   Expulsion from the professional accounting body.

   (e)   •   Being transparent with colleagues, customers and suppliers (points 1 & 2)
              •   Reporting financial and regulatory information clearly and on time (point 1)
              •   Paying suppliers a fair price and on time (points 3 & 4)
              •   Being open and honest by identifying when it is appropriate to accept gifts and hospitality (point 5)
              •   Providing fair treatment to employees (points 2, 6 & 7)

   (f)   The Code of Practice is not statutory, so not legally binding. It is a voluntary code which Frances, Philips and Nightingale chooses to apply as best practice.

Task 7

(a)   This is a bribe or inducement and Steve could be charged with the criminal offence of bribery.

(b)   Objectivity – Magda, and hence Frances, Philips and Nightingale, is being offered the opportunity of working for a bigger client if The Growing Business successfully takes over Greenshoots Nursery.

Confidentiality – Magda has confidential information about the financial difficulties facing Greenshoots nursery which would be beneficial to The Growing Business when considering what price to offer Steve for the business.

(c)   Two of:

   •   immediately inform both The Growing Business and Greenshoots nursery that she deals with both clients.

   •   identify any existing procedures that Frances, Philip and Nightingale have in place to address a conflict of interest between two clients.

   •   inform her manager of the conflict she is facing and document any discussions she has.

   •   consider whether she is able to act for either client in this situation due to her knowledge of both clients. It may be better if she does not work on either of these clients during the takeover negotiations as each may perceive that she will use confidential information to assist the other.

Task 8

(a)   Lisa must explain to the directors that she, and therefore Frances, Philips and Nightingale, can no longer act for Chicago Diner Ltd. The taxes that it should have paid to HMRC have been dishonestly retained by the business and so become criminal property. This amounts to money laundering on the part of Chicago Diner Ltd.

(b)   **(1)**   The Money Laundering Reporting Officer (MLRO) at Frances, Philips and Nightingale.

   (2)   Two of:

   •   the identity of the person(s) involved in money laundering, including full names, addresses, telephone numbers, dates of birth, account details

   •   Information on which the suspicion of money laundering is based

   •   the whereabouts of the laundered property if known

(c)   If Lisa does not report the tax error, she may then also be charged with money laundering. She will have committed a crime 'failure to disclose' and could be imprisoned for up to five years and/or face an unlimited fined. She would also face disciplinary action from her professional accounting body.

Task 9

(a)   No

(b)   Environmental protection – protecting the environment by conserving resources so that they are available in the long term

Social equality – focusing on the wellbeing of employees and the communities and societies they belong to and affect

Economic growth – increasing profits but not at the expense of society, employees or the environment

(c)   Three of the following:

- ensure suppliers are using sustainably produced paper and paper products
- use production methods to minimise the use of harmful chemicals and waste
- employ and train local people to support the local community
- undertake apprenticeships to employ young people in the area
- sponsor a local sports team
- measure performance against sustainability targets

Note: any other reasonable suggestions supporting environmental, social or economic sustainability would be accepted

for your notes

for your notes

for your notes